FIRST EDITION
LUSH COMICS & PLASTIC CRIMEWAVE 2014
PRINTED IN THE UK

© TEXT: LUSH LTD
© ARTWORK: LUSH LTD & PLASTIC CRIMEWAVE

ISBN 978-0-9927082-3-8   PLU 26693
www.lush.co.uk

SPECIAL THANKS TO VICKY, ELOISE, KC, DAWN, ROWENA & MARK
DEDICATED TO MICHEL POINT

ON THE TRAIL OF SANDALWOOD SMUGGLERS

LUSH COMICS
AND
PLASTIC CRIMEWAVE

PLOTTING-SIMON CONSTANTINE, AGNÈS GENDRY, MATT FAIRHALL
WRITTEN BY- SIMON, AGNÈS, MATT & PLASTIC CRIMEWAVE
ART BY- PLASTIC CRIMEWAVE
COLOURS & DESIGN BY- ADAM KRAKOW
BACK COVER & SPINE DESIGN BY- ADAM GOSWELL

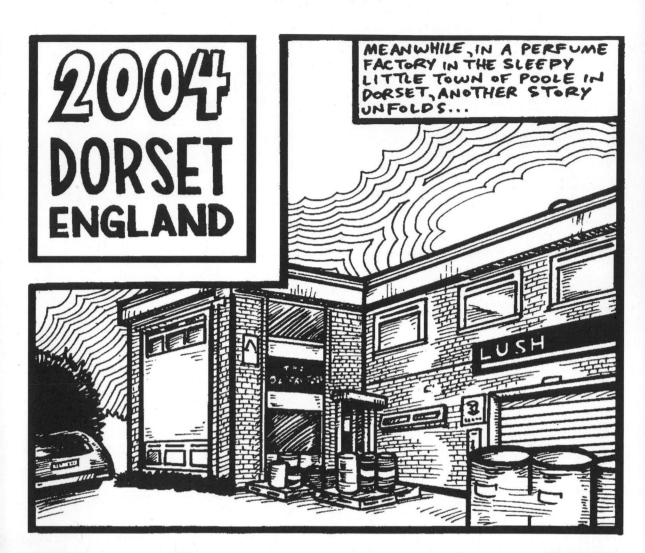

2004
DORSET
ENGLAND

MEANWHILE, IN A PERFUME FACTORY IN THE SLEEPY LITTLE TOWN OF POOLE IN DORSET, ANOTHER STORY UNFOLDS...

SIMON CONSTANTINE & AGNÈS GENDRY BECOME FRIENDS.

THEY SPEND THEIR DAYS
SOURCING QUALITY
ESSENTIAL OILS FOR
PRODUCTS...

DISTILLED FROM PLANTS,
THESE OILS HAVE A LONG
HISTORY OF BEING USED
TO PROTECT US FROM
DISEASE, OR TO ATTRACT.

SHOCKINGLY, SIMON & AGNÈS
ONE DAY DISCOVERED THAT
MANY OILS THEY'D OBTAINED
WERE MIXED WITH SYNTH-
ETIC CHEMICALS, & WEREN'T
AS PURE AS THEIR SUPPLIERS
HAD ASSURED.

SOMETHING HAD TO BE DONE!

RUMOURS SOON REACH THEM OF SHADY SANDALWOOD OIL DEALINGS, AND THEY DECIDE TO INVESTIGATE

I'VE BEEN HEARING BAD THINGS ABOUT INDIAN SANDALWOOD.

WHAT KIND OF THINGS?

OUR INDIAN BUSINESS PARTNERS MENTIONED THEIR NEIGHBOURS WERE ATTACKED OVER SANDALWOOD.

WHAT HAPPENED?

SO THE WAFTY WAYFARERS WENT TO NEW CALEDONIA AND SOON FOUND THEMSELVES ON A TRAIL OF SMUGGLING, MURDER, DECEIT AND DECAPITATION...

HERE THEY MEET UP WITH THE SUPPLIER OF THIS SANDALWOOD, A 60-YEAR OLD FRENCH ADVENTURER AND RASCAL NAMED MICHEL POINT.

HOW DID YOU END UP LIVING HERE? IT'S VERY FAR FROM HOME... *

THEY THINK I DON'T SPEAK FRENCH...

WELL, I LIVED IN TAHITI FOR A TIME (AH, THE WOMEN THERE ARE SO BEAUTIFUL) AND THEN I ENDED UP HERE. IT'S A LONG STORY! *

*SPEAKING IN FRENCH

SOUNDS LIKE IT! WE HEAR THERE'S A BIG MARKET FOR SANDALWOOD, HAS ANYONE TRIED TO STEAL IT FROM HERE?

I DO.

AGNÈS, MA CHÈRE, THE KANAKS ARE FIERCELY PROUD OF THEIR ANCESTRAL LAND, THERE IS NO WAY THEY WOULD LET THAT HAPPEN.

GOOD LUCK TO ANYONE WHO TRIES TO STEAL TREES FROM THEM, I DON'T FANCY THEIR CHANCES!

THE KANAKS ARE THE INDIGENOUS PEOPLE OF NEW CALEDONIA

THEY HAVE A RICH AND FORMIDABLE CULTURAL HERITAGE...

LIVING UNDER FRENCH COLONIAL RULE SINCE 1853, THEY HAVE FOUGHT SEVERAL BLOODY BATTLES FOR THEIR INDEPENDENCE.

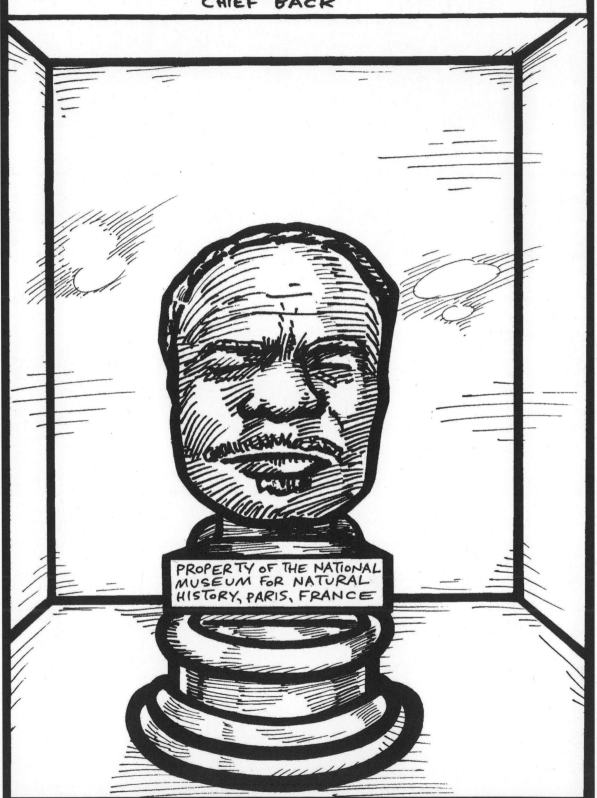

"THESE TREES GROW ON OUR ANCESTRAL LANDS"

"WE DIG THEM UP, ROOTS 'N ALL, AND AT THEIR CENTRE LIES THE OIL RICH HEARTWOOD"

NOT ONE PART OF THE PRECIOUS TREE IS WASTED.

AUSTRALIA

STILL HOT ON THE TRAIL FOR SUSTAINABLE SOURCES OF SANDALWOOD, WE FIND THE DOUGHTY DUO IN THE LAST FRONTIER, KUNUNURRA, WESTERN AUSTRALIA.

HERE A NEW VENTURE GROWING INDIAN SANDALWOOD HAS BEGUN...

THIS REMARKABLE PROJECT HAS CRACKED THE PROBLEM OF HOW TO GROW INDIAN SANDALWOOD TREES.

THESE TREES ARE ACTUALLY PARASITIC....

THEIR ROOTS BURY INTO THE GROUND, AND SUCK LIFE FROM NEIGHBOURING PLANTS LIKE A VAMPIRE DRAWS BLOOD...

WHY IS THIS WOOD GROWN HERE AND NOT INDIA?

IT'S TOO MUCH OF A SECURITY THREAT TO GROW THERE.

OK ISN'T THERE AN AUSTRALIAN SANDALWOOD AS WELL AS INDIAN?

THERE IS, LET'S GO FIND IT!

SOMEWHERE LOST IN THE OUTBACK...

OUR WALKABOUT WANDERERS MEET WITH ABORIGINAL FARMERS TO FIND OUT MORE ABOUT AUSTRALIAN SANDALWOOD

THE ROUGH AND READY ENVIRONMENT SUITS THE LOCAL SPECIES OF SANDALWOOD WELL.

THEY SOON MEET KEITH SKEGGY, AN ABORIGINAL MAN WHO HARVESTS WOOD.

SIMON & AGNÈS HEAD FOR KALGOORLIE, A NEARBY MINING POST, AND HOME TO THE INFAMOUS 'SUPER PIT', A VAST OPEN CUT GOLD MINE.

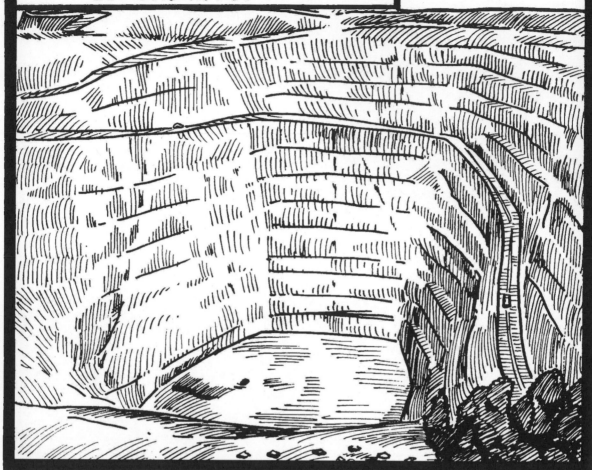

THEY MAKE FOR A LOCAL WATERING HOLE TO REFLECT ON THEIR JOURNEY SO FAR...

INDIAN SANDALWOOD OIL IS WORTH £1500 A KILO

...IT HAS BEEN SMUGGLED THROUGHOUT THE AGES FOR...

SACRED TEMPLE CARVINGS...

INCENSE

CREMATION...

FOR RELIGIOUS RITUALS...

AND OTHER BURIAL RITES LIKE...

FUNERAL PYRES...

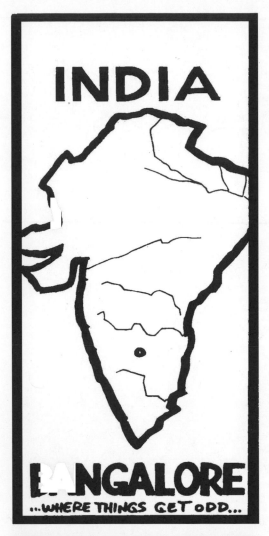

INDIA

BANGALORE

...WHERE THINGS GET ODD...

AN ANONYMOUS SOURCE ARRANGES FOR OUR PERFUMED PILGRIMS TO RENDEZVOUS WITH A PAIR OF ILLICIT SANDALWOOD TRADERS...

RIGHTO, THIS SHOULD BE INTERESTING.

WE MIGHT NEED TO KEEP A LOW PROFILE AND GO INCOGNITO.

THIS SHOULD DO THE TRICK!

TAKE THAT STUPID THING OFF.

WE HAVE TO PRETEND WE'RE INTERESTED IN BUYING FROM THIS DODGY DUO. DON'T GIVE US AWAY!

BUT NEVER FOUND OUT WHERE THEY GOT THEIR SANDALWOOD FROM...

OUR SCENTED VAGABONDS HAD QUESTIONS FOR THE ROGUE TRADERS...

THESE TRADERS WERE KEEN TO DO BUSINESS, BUT THEY WERE SMALL FRY. SIMON & AGNÈS WANTED TO SPEAK TO THE "BIG BOSS" OF SANDALWOOD THEY'D HEARD RUMOURS OF...

THE MYSTERIOUS SOURCE ARRANGES THE MEETING AND THEY SOAR THROUGH THE SKIES TO GOA...

...WHERE A BLACKED-OUT MERCEDES LAYS IN WAIT. THEY HAVE NO IDEA WHERE THEY ARE BEING TAKEN.

GOA

LOCATED IN WEST INDIA, ITS SMALLEST STATE

SIMON & AGNÈS WERE HEADED TO AN ILLEGAL FACTORY AND THEY WERE BOTH APPREHENSIVE & EXCITED.

SURPRISINGLY, THEY PULLED UP TO A HOUSE ON A SUBURBAN STREET.

AFTER CLAIMING ALL THESE QUESTIONS WERE "TRADE SECRETS" THEY AGREED TO CALL "THE BIG BOSS"

THE INFORMATION GIVEN BACK WAS VAGUE, BUT THE BOSS SAID THEY'D NEVER RUN OUT OF WOOD AND SUPPLIED ALL THE BIG PERFUME & FRAGRANCE COMPANIES.

"THE BOSS" ALSO SAID HE TRACKED ALL THE SANDAL-WOOD IN FIJI & INDONESIA, AND THAT HE CONTROLLED THE WHOLE MARKET AND PRICING...

WHO WAS "THE BOSS"?

SO THE NEXT STEP WAS...

NEW DELHI

TO A HOTEL WHERE "THE BOSS" ALSO KNOWN AS "THE DON" HAD AGREED TO MEET

WAITING ANXIOUSLY IN THEIR HOTEL LOBBY, OUR INTREPID EXPLORERS CATCH A GLIMPSE OF HIM.

BLIMEY, WHAT'S THAT BODYGUARD GOT IN HIS POCKET, AGNÈS?

THAT'S A GUN ON A CHAIN, SIMON!

PHEW! I JUST THOUGHT HE WAS PLEASED TO SEE US!

SIMON & AGNÈS ASK "THE DON" ABOUT STORIES THEY'VE HEARD OF A LEGENDARY SANDALWOOD POACHER, A MAN CALLED VEERAPPAN.

WHO WAS VEERAPPAN?

JAN. 18 1952 GOPINATHAM

IN THE SMALL VILLAGE OF KARNATAKA THE INFAMOUS VEERAPPAN IS BORN TO A FAMILY OF CATTLE GRAZERS.

AS A CHILD, HE WAS KNOWN AS MOLAKAI, AND HE ALSO SUFFERED FROM ASTHMA

1962 WAS HIS FIRST KILLING-AT AGE 10! HE SHOT DOWN A "TUSKER" WITH HELP FROM HIS GURU SEVI GOUNDER (WHO WAS ALSO HIS RELATIVE)

1970 – VEERAPPAN JOINED HIS FIRST GANG OF POACHERS AND BANDITS, CALLED A DACOIT IN INDIA

1972 – HE WAS FIRST ARRESTED ON SUSPICION OF STRANGLING ONE OF HIS OWN CHILDREN, FOR BEING THE THIRD SUCCESSIVE GIRL...

VEERAPPAN STARTED OUT AS A SMUGGLER OF SANDALWOOD AND IVORY, KILLING ELEPHANTS FOR THEIR TREASURE.

SOON VEERAPPAN GRADUATED TO KILLING MANY OF HIS ENEMIES, MOSTLY FOREST GUARDS - HE KILLED HIS FIRST NEAR KARNATAKA BECAUSE THE GUARD, K.M. PRITHVI, TRIED TO PREVENT HIS ELEPHANT POACHING IN 1983.

IN 1986 HE WAS JAILED AGAIN BUT ESCAPED UNDER MYSTERIOUS CIRCUMSTANCES— POSSIBLY BY BRIBING A POLICE OFFICER...

IN 1987 VEERAPPAN KIDNAPPED & THEN HACKED TO DEATH A FOREST OFFICER NAMED CHIDAMBARAM FROM TAMIL NADU. THIS MADE THE GOVERNMENT OFFICIALLY NOTICE HIS ACTIVITIES.

NOT TO MENTION HE KILLED 5 MEMBERS OF A RIVAL GANG THAT YEAR...

IN 1989 HE KILLED 3 FOREST RANGERS AFTER ABDUCTING THEM FROM BEGUR FOREST FOR 15 DAYS.

HIS SLAUGHTER OF THREE POLICEMEN AND A CONSTABLE NEAR HOGENAK IN 1990 LEAD TO THE CREATION OF A SPECIAL TASK FORCE THAT WAS SOON ON HIS TAIL.

IN FEBRUARY 1992, HIS LIEUTENANT GURUNATHAN WAS KILLED BY THE TASK FORCE.

SI SHAKEEL AHMED WAS SOLELY RESPONSIBLE FOR HIS CAPTURE & SLAYING

THREE MONTHS LATER, VEERAPPAN ATTACKED CHAMAR-AJANNAR POLICE STATION, KILLING POLICEMEN AND STEALING ARMS. IN AUGUST 1992, HE TOOK HIS REVENGE ON SHAKEEL AHMED, SLAYING HIM WITH A TRAP HE LAID USING A FALSE INFORMANT AS BAIT. THE SPECIAL TASK FORCE INTENSIFIED ITS EFFORTS, SCOURING KARNATAKA'S BORDERS & VEERAPPAN'S VILLAGE OF BIRTH FOR ITS ELUSIVE TARGET...

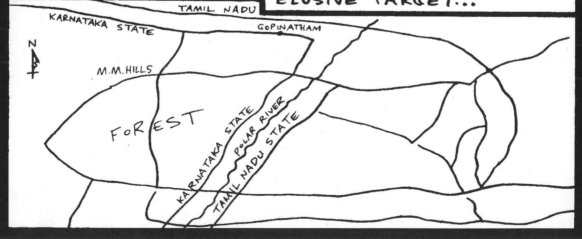

TAMIL NADU

KARNATAKA STATE

GOPINATHAM

N

M.M. HILLS

FOREST

KARNATAKA STATE

POLAR RIVER

TAMIL NADU STATE

AFTERWARDS, VEERAPPAN'S GANG WAS DOWN TO A MERE 5 MEMBERS

THE GOVERNMENT ARRESTED HIS WIFE IN 1993 FOR AIDING HIM...

BUT SHE WAS ACQUITED...

IN PERHAPS HIS BOLDEST MOVE, ON JULY 30, 2000, VEERAPPAN KIDNAPPED THE FAMOUS BOLLYWOOD STAR RAJKUMAR

RAJKUMAR'S SON-IN-LAW AND 2 OTHERS WERE ALSO TAKEN FROM DODDA GAJANUR, WHERE THE MOVIE STAR WAS AT A HOUSEWARMING PARTY

THE PUBLIC WENT MAD!

THE GOVERNMENT FELL INTO DISARRAY...

VIOLENCE BROKE OUT IN BANGALORE & KARNATAKA, EVEN A STRIKE WAS ENACTED IN SEPTEMBER, AND KARNATAKA'S CHIEF MINISTER GOT INVOLVED...

R.GOPAL, AN EDITOR AT THE TAMIL MAGAZINE NAKKEERAN, WAS BROUGHT IN AS A NEGOTIATOR.

VEERAPPAN HAD DEMANDS TO RELEASE POLITICAL EXTREMISTS, AND AFTER 109 DAYS HE FINALLY RELEASED THE BOLLYWOOD STAR UNHARMED.

AFTER KIDNAPPING & KILLING COUNTLESS OFFICIALS, SETTING TRAPS WITH LANDMINES, AND GAINING SUPPORT FROM TAMIL NATIONALIST ORGANIZATIONS, 50,000,000 RUPEES (1.25 MILLION USA) WAS OFFERED FOR VEERAPPAN. ON OCTOBER 18, 2004 VEERAPPAN & 2 OF HIS MEN WERE SLAIN BY THE TAMIL NADU SPECIAL TASK FORCE HEADED UP BY K. VIJAY KUMAR, IN THE VILLAGE OF PAPPARAPATTI. VEERAPPAN & HIS CREW WERE LURED INTO AN AMBULANCE FOR MEDICAL TREATMENT. CALLED "OPERATION COCOON," THE FORCE SURROUNDED THE VEHICLE AND A FATAL GUN BATTLE ENSUED. THOUSANDS TURNED OUT FOR HIS FUNERAL, & A FILM BASED ON VEERAPPAN'S LIFE CALLED "VANA YUDDHAM" WAS MADE IN 2013.

BACK AT THE OL' FACTORY IN POOLE

I THINK WE GOT MORE THAN WE BARGAINED FOR ON OUR TRIP AGNES.

I CAN'T BELIEVE SOME OF THE THINGS THAT HAPPENED!

IT SEEMS NO MATTER WHERE WE FIND SANDAL-WOOD IT'S ALWAYS THE SAME RESULT.

SMUGGLING, DECEIT, GREED... IT'S A MINE-FIELD OUT THERE!

THANK GOOD-NESS YOU FOUND SOME DECENT SOURCES, FOR NOW AT LEAST.

AS WE PREPARE TO BID FAREWELL, WE SHOULD LEAVE YOU WITH A WARNING. ONCE YOU LET THE PARASTIC ROOTS OF SANDALWOOD TAKE HOLD OF YOUR HEART, BEWARE—ITS SWEET AND INTOXICATING NATURE CAN EASILY TURN YOU TO DUPLICITY AND DEVILRY. OUR DARING DUO NAVIGATED THIS TREACHEROUS WORLD AND WERE LUCKY... YOU MIGHT NOT BE...

WHERE TO NEXT?

WHY DO I HAVE TO DECIDE?

HAVE YOU GOT THE RIGHT SHOES?

THE END